Dedicated to my two beauties
Hannah Rose and Daniel Jack
You are my puffins and turtle doves.

First published November 2015 by Vandings Way House

www.vandingswayhouse.com

Special thanks to Tim Matthews for his help
on legal matters and publishing.

Designed by Evolve Creative

www.evolvecreative.biz

Printed by Evolve Print

www.evolve-print.com

ISBN: 978-0-9934437-4-9

Foreword

This has been a very emotional project for me. I am filled with joy and appreciation for all the contributions that you have agreed to share. My gratitude is overwhelming.

We all experience love and loss and everything in-between, and sometimes find it hard to talk about. I have found counselling, journalling, meditating, painting, playing tennis, and photography life-affirming, but most of all the love of you, your closeness, and your warm spirit has helped me grow and develop as a person. I hope it helps you too. Often meaningful conversations are the best ones, whether through poetry, short stories, or simple musings on life, thus this wonderful project.

All profits raised from this book will go to the Ovarian Cancer Action Research Centre at Hammersmith Hospital, where I am being treated, to help other women and their families. May it also raise awareness of the symptoms of Ovarian Cancer and thus help early diagnosis, and therefore better prognosis.

Thank you.

Florence

Symptoms and what to do

Watch out for these ovarian cancer symptoms:

- Persistent stomach pain
- Persistent bloating
- Finding it difficult to eat or feeling full quickly
- Needing to wee more often

Other symptoms you may notice include:

- Back pain
- Changes in your bowel habits (diarrhoea or constipation)
- Feeling tired all the time

If you're regularly experiencing these symptoms on most days it's important to talk to your GP as soon as possible.

Download our mobile phone symptoms diary app to record the symptoms of ovarian cancer on your phone by searching for 'Ovarian Cancer Action' in the App Store of your phone. You can email yourself a summary report to take with you to your GP.

www.ovarian.org.uk/symptoms

www.ovarian.org.uk/symptomsdiary

Ovarian cancer is the fifth most common cancer in women, with around 7,000 women diagnosed in the UK every year.

Not many people have heard of ovarian cancer so it is often diagnosed late - making it the UK's most deadly gynaecological disease.

If members of your family have ovarian or breast cancer you may be at an increased risk of developing ovarian cancer yourself.

This is because families can pass down mutations in the BRCA gene that increase risk of ovarian cancer.

It is important to remember that the BRCA gene mutation is not the only gene mutation that contributes to a woman's risk of developing ovarian cancer.

You can use Ovarian Cancer Action's online BRCA Risk Tool to explore whether your family history puts you at risk of ovarian cancer:

www.ovarian.org.uk/BRCARiskTool

Details of the Research Centre

Ovarian Cancer Action fund world-class scientific research at the Ovarian Cancer Action Research Centre, the only dedicated research centre for ovarian cancer in the UK.

Treatment for ovarian cancer is not as advanced as treatment for other, better-known cancers like breast and prostate cancer.

Ovarian Cancer Action want to make ovarian cancer treatment more effective and reduce the number of women who die from the disease.

Ovarian Cancer Action only fund research that can be translated into meaningful outcomes for real women.

The Ovarian Cancer Action Research Centre drives new and more targeted treatments from pre-clinical studies, to clinical trials and into gynaecological clinics across the UK.

www.ovarian.org.uk/research

Please watch this powerful film about The Ovarian Cancer Action Research Centre:

youtu.be/amyovmSqgGA

All money raised from this project will go to the research Centre, to build a better future for women with Ovarian Cancer.

Ovarian Cancer Action Contact Details

Website: **http://www.ovarian.org.uk/**

Twitter: **@ovariancanceruk**

Email: **info@ovarian.org.uk**

Telephone: **020 7380 1730**

Contents

Teaching of Ovarian Care

Who is Florence? What is she
That all her friends commend her?
Good and fair and wise is she
So poems we must send her
That her book may come to be.

She is kind and she is fair.
So evident is her kindness
Teaching us of ovarian care
To reduce symptom blindness.
We have to support her there.

Then to Florence let us sing
That Florence is excelling.
Her book is an inspiring thing,
Which in her heart is dwelling.
To her let us poems bring.

Margaret Beresford

Take the Crown

Florence asked me for a poem
And I promised her I'd write one
Oh dear she needs it by tomorrow
But ideas I have simply none

Ms Wilks I am so sorry
Didn't mean to let you down
Cause when it comes to raising money
Then you truly take the crown

Marian Diviney

Summer!

Absorbing heat from the sun,
Jumping over waves,
Laughter all around!
Morning strolls with friends,
Lunchtime snacks in the park,
Nothing better than summer fun!
Adventures await us all,
Whether you're big or small,
Smiles are abroad!
Family time is the best,
With cousins and aunties,
Uncles and more!
I love summertime the best of all!

Olivia Maieli, age 10

Autumn

Blustery wind flicking leaves into the air,
Farmers picking potatoes in the freshly ploughed fields.
Fruits in the hedgerows giving up their treasure,
Leaves different colours; ruby red, glowing orange, green,
blue and yellow.
Children in wellies splashing and laughing in muddy puddles,
People wrapped warm in scarves and hats in the foggy
morning air.

Zoe Cardy, aged 8

Heavenly Father

Today looking back on my day, I felt your presence near me
It was like you were talking to me, through the prayer
Your presence lightened up my day, and made me happy,
You were saying, be enlightened, that you love me
As much as my parents do.
When I was sad I prayed and you helped me
And made me happy for the rest of the day
Thank you for this
I hope you will be with me for the rest of my life
And I will pray to you, I know I can trust you
You will always be there for me and my family
That's why I pray for you to help me and others in need
I would like to share you love and compassion with others
Father in your mercy, hear my prayer.
Amen.

Lukasz Sloma, aged 11

Tuesday 20th October 2015

About Tracey/Fairy

Tracey you are the coloured Sparkles Sprinkerly on my art pictures.

Tracey you are the shiny yellow sun gleaming aiganst my bright pink cheeks.

Tracey you are the Shiny White Stars blinking in patterns in the navy bouncy night Sky.

by Audrey Tsantilis-Lodge.

Age: Seven

About Tracey/Fairy

This poem is about Audrey's Fairy Godmother, Tracey Weatherill who died in December 2009 aged 41 of Ovarian Cancer

Audrey Tsantilis-Lodge, aged 7

Joe-isms (Age 3)

'Joe, when are you going to do as you're told'
'Hmm... in August'

'I'm NOT ticklish! I'm Irish!'

'Sometimes mummy, coughing helps the trumps to come'

'Joe, did you put anything in the car CD player'
'Yes I did mummy... I fed him some money!'

'Mummy, when I am older I am going to take you for a drive in my Ferrari'
'Oh lovely, well it's good to aim high hon. I will buy a new dress'
'Yes and I will buy a new dress too' Hmm.

Joseph Daire Arthurworrey

A Recipe for Friendship

This is how to make a most wonderfully brilliant friendship! So whip up your ingredients and get baking!!!

- 1 cup of happiness
- 3 teaspoons of forgiveness
- 800g of thoughtfulness
- 700ml of care
- 3 tablespoons of trust
- 100g of loyalty
- 8000 tablespoons of kindness
- 8 teaspoons of support
- 80ml of love
- 300g of fun

For The Icing
- 800g of more kindness

Method:
- Firstly take your care, trust, loyalty, and love and put them into your magical mixing bowl. Mix these well with 700ml of care.
- Secondly take a separate bowl and put your fun, support, kindness and happiness into it. Whisk with a fork until wonderfully smooth.
- Gently pour this into your first bowl bit by bit.
- Lastly you want to take your forgiveness and thoughtfulness and put them into the bowl whilst mixing with the other hand.

How to make the icing:
- Put your 800g of kindness into a squeezy bag and pipe onto your friendship.
- Bake for extra.

Georgie Greig, aged 10

The Midnight Fox

Silent but deadly, cautious with stealth,
Eyes as green as emeralds, sly yet shy
Hunter but hunted, protector of her clan
That is the Midnight Fox, the Midnight Fox, the Midnight Fox.

Regal and beautiful, she stalks through the night
A tail with such beauty, eyes black as coal
She shows no mercy to her prey
That is the Midnight Fox, the Midnight Fox, the Midnight Fox.

Hunted by man, always careful and cunning,
When the gun goes BANG, she graciously flees,
Back to the den, where her little ones feed
That is the Midnight Fox, the Midnight Fox, the Midnight Fox.

Maisie Duff, aged 10

Inspired by the book The Midnight Fox

Dylan Thomas

Dylan was a famous poet,
Every rhyme he would know it,
He was born in Swansea, Wales,
Where the weather often gales,
He was best in his school year,
He usually wrote about fear,
His alcohol led to his death (Beer),
He was the envy of his friends at school
He liked to go to the swimming pool,
Dylan was a famous poet,
Every rhyme he would know it.

Maurice Chapple Wise, aged 9

*With help from his friends at Ealing
and Hammersmith Woodcraft Folk*

George & Fred

Scrumptious little pups
Charming puppy face
They both love to play
Especially to chase.

Puppy love
So pure and sweet
Using their paws
To tap each other's feet

You've gotta love watching puppies
Run around and play
Nibbling on each other's ears
Kissing and licking away

Always together
Biting each other's tails
Nothing is better than puppy love
It never fails

Hungry little Fred
Sometimes he's very quiet
Fond of a loaf of bread
Will he need to go on a diet?

Stunning young George
He once swallowed three collars
He does like to gorge
But he's worth a million dollars

The pups love the kitchen
There's always a chance to eat
The best friend of men
Watch out for the ovens heat

George and Fred
A present from above
They are always in your head
Simply adorable and full of love

Andrew Lee

Breakfast

I pace, she descends, eventually.
Trainers in hand... a delay.
We go out.

Woof bark! Woof bark!
I sound the alarm 'til my lead snaps me away.
6.07, a cat is declared.
We walk on, tail wagging.

I slow to sniff the ground,
In the darkness I'm allowed.
Chip located, I'm yanked away.
... Why?

We walk, chipper me, wagging.
I slow again, she likes this more.
'Good boy' I release a steaming trail.
... Why?

I wag on, nearly there.
Both, now, wide awake.
I hear, smell it, I tumble
Head long into my dream.
... Kibble.

She descends again, not dressed for walks or gardens.
... Why?

Charges me with a vital role; snooze and chew her
slipper just slightly.
It's called 'On Guard.'
I wag agreement to the task.
... Whatever.

Barney Judic, a golden retriever

How simple life could be, why over complicate it?

We live in a life/world
Where people judge on exterior
Judging books by their cover

As generations pass
New things come to trend

Technology where people hide behind lenses
And forget about the beauty of imagination.

Jason Martinez

Life

The more we live the closer we get in understanding life,

The more we love the closer we get in meaning of life.

Alfred Shahverdian

'Life is like a bunch of bananas - never straight(forward)'

Peter Domone

'We can't put the world to rights in an evening'

Vickie Domone

'I'd rather have a blank canvas and furnish it with life'

Mark Tugman

Life Achievement

As I lay posh
On my soft reclining leather chair,
Having had a such a sumptuous Sunday feast,
I reflect on my life with bellyful of pride.

Tears of joy trickle down my cheeks
As I know I have everything,
That any human being could dream of,
Such a luxury and my delightful family in my mansion.

My achievements baffle me sometimes.
Am I the very man with the same name?
Who cut the sugar cane in the shearing heat?
Never went to school to learn,
Shunted from house to house and place to place.

Yet within two score years I am completely changed.
It could be my determination and application,
My unfaltering ambition and faith,
My thirst for knowledge, and self improvement;

But I know the reason lies,
The fright of failure and lost of face,
Letting down my daddee and upbringing,
And returning to my roots with nothing to show.

Jay Woogara

In the Beginning

In the beginning we came together
To build a world full of best endeavour
Forming communities with common goals
Driven by our tireless human souls
Then friendships form without plan or reason
Ensuring passage through every season
Time passes by and friendships change
Some seem normal others seem strange
Feeding fuel into our hearts
Unaware of what departs
Like fear of difference that drives suspicion
Or values grasped without a mission
With community and friendship all is clear
Engage with lives and love comes near.

David Alderton

Friendship

When I am old and my steps are slow,
My eyes dim and my stamina low,
I'll sit in my chair, content til life ends,
That my life has been filled with such wonderful friends

This jigsaw puzzle that makes up me,
Is filled with friends and family,
The things we're taught – the good, the bad –
Our habits echo mum and dad

When life is hard and things go wrong,
It's always friends which keep us strong,
They'll challenge us to tasks which scare –
To strip off for a calendar dare!

To cycle naked around the city
(Not everyone was looking pretty!)
To create art with brush or pen,
To meet and eat and dance til ten... (or much later)

The tapestry which makes our life
With love and laughter woven tight,
Life's never dull and I'll smile til life ends,
Thinking 'Where would we be without our friends?!'

Elaine Hill

4 Peas in a Pod

I raise a glass to our beautiful friendship
Digby Stuart, Cowley Road, Catford,
Bromley, Chicago, Stamford Brook
Oh Malia, Bagni di Luca, Nice,
Salisbury, Bath, 4 peas in a pod,
Somerset House, Italian Fountains,
National Portrait Gallery, Boris Bikes,
Hyde Park, Muriel's Kitchen,
Serpentine's Lido, the Cotswolds.
Laughter, Honesty, Comfort
Chatter, trust, affection
The bond of students
Three out of four with a cancer
4 peas in a pod
Ignore it and live on

Florence Wilks

Le Wimo

Fun loving
Rebels
Inspirational
Ever lasting
Non conformist
Determined
Smiles ;-)

Dedicated to Florence Lee,
Lyn-Marie Williams & Lisa Moore

Lisa Godden

Over 30 Years of Friendship with Florence...

Quite fascinating
Certainly eventful
Definitely entertaining
Very delicious
At times challenging - writing a poem (chuckle, chuckle)
Occasionally tearful
But mostly bursting with sunny laughter and bliss
Treasured.
Florence – my enchanting, faithful friend.

Lyn-Marie Williams

With Her

Where do we stand
After our youth
Behaving square
Not a chance
Ligging and gigging
Where we can
For what else is there
As we get older
She's just as lovely
As when I first saw her
Moves like a siren
Got to get with her
Taking the lead
And talking to her
We'll have a beer
And take in a band
Imagine our youth
Without the angst

Oksob

French Evening

The silence is eternal
on this humid evening
of trees,
clinging to the sky like sweat-drenched shirts
and the crunch of gravel
violates the quiet dampness
Honeysuckle scent
drugs the night air
with crazed delight,
holding moths and bats in frenetic daze.
While the jealous moon,
old voyeur,
hardly breathing, leaves
his misty breath
on the cold-windowed sky
as lovers cling
in dewy embrace.

John Green

Better than Benedict

Mr Cumberbatch dipped in chocolate,
What could be better than that?
The lump in my throat from a heartfelt note?
Or the soothing purr of a cat?

Maybe the gleam of a wood stove,
On an inky winter's night?
Or the musical show of a wild meadow
As birds and bugs unite?

Ah, the smell of bread in the oven,
That surely has a chance?
Or the relief you earn from a complete tax return
When you really hate finance?

I must confess to the wondrousness
Of the feel of clean bedsheets
Add to this, my son's toothpasty kiss
And life could be complete.

Oh I nearly forgot, the joy of a hot-
water bottle upon my aches,
And the glorious sight, the sheer spongy delight
Of a bakery full of cakes.

How about a lazy morning
Of pyjamas and sofas and toast?
Or a board of cheese? A puppy's sneeze?
Maybe those I love the most.

The final rivals to my heart?
A smile when I'm feeling small,
A gentle touch when life gets too much,
This really must beat them all?

But I already know the answer,
And my friend, you should know it too,
What betters my days and a million clichés?
The bigness of my love for you.

Juliet Staveley

And then I Saw Him

It had been the darkest of times,
I had been searching and found only the faintest of glows,
And then I saw him

His own light dimmed by disappointment,
but shining like a beacon to me.
I couldn't understand why nobody else could see him as
brightly as I did.
I'm pleased they couldn't.

Neither of us planned on being there that night,
I'll go with fate, he'll go with god,
sometimes even we disagree...

And now, together, our light shines brightest of all,
enveloping all around us, with laughter, tears, dogs, small
humans, friends, and love. Above all else, don't forget
and never give up, on love...

Lara Henshaw, 42 and ¾

Breathe

I am grateful for many things in life,
But most of all for the two butterfly wings,
That flap and flutter inside me.

In, out, in, out, in, out.
Quietly, without reward or recognition,
Just pulmonary determination.

Bagpipes that play my tune.
Marking days with a sinuous beauty,
Filling dreams with pure air.

There have been times when,
Full of self-pity, I would have stopped,
But for this duo that flank my heart.

They know something I don't.
They know it's worth pushing on.
It is always worth pushing on.

In an erratic world, they are my constants.
Obstinate, impish, glorious lungs:
What else can I do but thank you?

Juliet Staveley

Held

I hold you in my heart
and in my aching head.

In my dreams I hold you, laughing with me, your hand in mine.
You are small again as I brush your hair.
At other times you are shadowy,
mouth forming words I strain to hear.
You are by turns angry, accusing, silent, a wall between us.
You are older.
I cannot envisage this new you, even in my sleep.

In my body I still feel you as you were, growing :
first a fluttering, then an ever heavier force to be reckoned with.
I am physically bereft -
empty with the lack of you.

I held you in my arms, encircling you.
But doubt sown, malignant, twisted my words into worms,
my deeds into demons, repainted your pictures.
How can I reach you through all this dust and destruction?

I hold you in my heart
and in my aching head.
Always.

Nina Robertson

I Still Don't Know What to Say

I know I should, what holds me back

The difficulties in my head

I'm not the sufferer

But I behave

Like the one who's in their bed

Been to talks by you

Fund raised for you

You've explained your pains and joy

Admiration too small a word

Yet I still don't know

How to talk to you

And if I can't

What happens when others, family, suffer

Or I myself am diagnosed

Any wonder that I stutter

My problem not yours

But no easier to talk to you

I saw you the other day

From afar let you walk by

I hurt inside and hope and pray

Next time I'll know what to say

What holds me back, what is my demon

Why such a coward, where is my fear

Then through mists parting light

Mortality unfaced my cross appears

Maybe now I can talk to you and you can help my fight

Kim Hughes

New Friend

No linear line can tame
A connection
The soul in boundless joy
I see you Feisty Twin
Angela Breheny

A Stranger's Smile

Just when you think nothing is there
You will find strength and shed despair
For that kind glance from someone's mind
Means that you are amongst human kind
And if you think they do not care
Think on what they may have to bear
So share that smile which is your gift
Stand tall move up as change is swift

Tim Matthews

Let Me Share

Let me share with you
My few crusts of thought
My last drops of wine-dark love
Take my humble soul
And my hungry mouth
Soak up my body's warmth
Pluck the stars from my eyes
And fly free on the milky way of my sheltering night

John Green

The Magnificent Spirit of You

Trust, with its gentle whisper the touch of eternal light
Cherish the world that lies within your soul
Know the sweetness of a shared embrace
Celebrate the magnificent spirit of you

Philippa Mukherjee

Life is Good!

Great is the morning
Another day dawns
Anticipating what's coming my way
Life is good!

Great is the morning
Sunshine or rain
Tennis, bridge or even work
Life is good!

Great is the evening
As darkness falls
Family meals or wine with friends
Life is good!

Jane Cooper

Que es Poesía?

Que es poesía?
Tu me preguntaste, mi amor
Que es poesía?
Eres tú, mi corazón.

Translation:
What is poetry?
You are asking me, my love
What is poetry?
It is you, my sweetheart.

Katya Addiego

Woohoo

What a life
Our family home is up for sale
WHY why Why

My beautiful baby girl is grown up
She's far away in Australia
Happy and safe and settled.
How marvellous

My lovely boy is being set adrift
Gaming is his passion
Who am I to judge
If he's within 800 out of all the European talent
Why won't he go on to succeed

Now our life will change
Me and Martin are abandoning ship
Poor Max the dog where is he, where are we?
Bring it on - life according to Florence Wilks is OK by me
My hero

Jane Coulthard

A House

A house is just a house
Memories in every room
Lively, full of life
A home
But what when everyone's gone?
Memories still remain
Haunting you
Taunting you
Why do they stay?
A house is just a house
But when everyone's gone
It's a prison
A prison of your own making
Every room holds a moment
But when the moments gone
When the persons gone
Wounds don't heal like they used to
Memories don't fade like photographs
Love doesn't leave when you want it to
What happens then?
When you're all alone?
Is a house still just a house?

Eleanor Coulthard

Poem of Love

I want to write you a poem of love
as opposed to a love poem
words bursting
full with life
vibrancy
veins pulsing redness like blush
mixed with bubbles of oxygen
Mine... my air
My blood
My life touching yours
for moments
for now
I look forward
am looking forward
to all
to every time
excitedly
my head is held high and greeting the land
as it appears in the distance

I find myself suddenly cradled in the purest joy of our togetherness
of mattering
To you.
it is immense
For me.

A lifetime striped with aloneness
of wishing
of watching
of wanting
of accepting
distance and separateness
even during alleged togetherness
circled by rings and vows and mixed clothing in wardrobes.
Futures allegedly mapped.

And now
After all this time
These months and seasons and on and so forth of insignificance.
I feel differently.

It is the sweetest, almost musical, feeling I know
laughter unbridled and free
a dancing spirit.
Mine, I see.
My body is filling and falling without gravity and flying
... weightless
time has no matter and
I feel lost with you.
In you.
Breathing your breath.
Intense.
... to let go
... to gently hold you in close
... to wait
... to care
... to give freely
to let you near.

Diana Hunter

Sunflower

Tow'ring sunflower
Turn your seedy face to me
Buersting with bounty

Quince

Sweetly perfumed quince
Your velvety golden skin
Scents the air I breathe

Emily Bishop

Musings of a GP

I was asked to write a musing of a GP
My thoughts went blank somewhat a degree
Never wanted to be a GP, paediatrics was my desire,
But sometimes in life we think about what we require.
A string of Jobs for General Practice took me to an interview
And I was accepted along with the chosen few.
Paediatrics, A&E, obstetrics, General Medicine and ENT
Also including 12 months as a GP trainee.
Fully qualified I returned to my paediatric dream
But overwhelmed with hospital bureaucracy decided to go back to the GP team.
Children are part of families, with parents, siblings, grannies and grandpas too
Patients in the cottage hospital and birthing unit, long stay hospital to visit and view
I wanted to be part of a community, providing a service to all ages with acute and chronic illnesses as well

I started as a GP in South Wales amongst hard grafting men
Chiselling out diamond coal, damaging their lungs again and again
I loved their humour, their ongoing rugby banter, their voices in full swing
Helping them get enough breath to get to the club, that was the important thing
I watched them live a life of courage, I watched them dying a death of suffering
I was part of a great primary care team who took an important part in everything
Patients and staff alike taught me how to care holistically and what empathy really meant
Children with cystic fibrosis and spina bifida who helped with ways to treat and prevent
The high prevalence in this place pioneered the vital research to lead to what we now see.
Now all women take folic acid in pregnancy and others benefit from stem cell therapy
I loved my work in the Llynfi valley even on those wet cold days and nights serving the people
The hours were long the work was tough but the great rewards there was nothing to equal
I had become part of a community, in fact I was the newsagent's daughter now come back what better compliment than that!

Then the knight in white armour swept me off my feet to pastures new
I was married in London cheered on by the bus load from Llynfi too
Then after 3 children gradually returned to General Practice in Ealing
What a contrast, a culture shock for me but the new challenge was appealing
Lords and homeless , patients spanning the World from all occupations including the BBC,
Unimaginable varied diseases as well as patients from every trouble spot in the globe to see.
A high prevalence of severely mentally ill often neglected by primary care
But not forgetting those with the stresses of everyday life you have to be aware
Medical students, astounded by the amount of serious disease attend the surgery frequently
We care for diabetics, asthmatics, COPD and heart and stroke patients in the community.
We keenly look out for cancer patients to diagnose early and provide supportive care
Our team look after pregnant ladies and along with families and children's welfare
I have now become part of this community and despite national low morale I am passionate about my work as an ordinary GP.

Dr Jacqueline Bayer

The Interloper

You weren't invited but you went along to the party anyway,
Interloper, you lurked silent and unnoticed in a space beside the cooker
You saw her laughing and felt a pang of something you could not define
Beady eyed you waited until every guest had left
While she tidied up the beer cans and cocktail sticks you hid in a cupboard

At first she didn't notice she had a house mate
You kept quiet, ate very little: bits of food hiding at the back of the fridge
A cucumber on the turn, a leaking tube of tomato paste, frozen cocktail sausages
When she was out, you lay on her bed and looked out at the sky
Beyond her joyful billowing curtains and felt something you couldn't define

But you became bored and audacious, you left hints that she was not alone
A scatter of frozen peas cast across the floor, mail ripped open on the hall carpet
She must be imagining things surely (everyone decided)
The work stress was causing this, even her GP agreed

She started to doubt herself, since when had she got so messy?
Clothes strewn across the floor, a lost earring, the TV left on
One day a running tap that leaked through the neighbours ceiling
No sooner fixed before it happened again

Your hunger became voracious, her fridge emptied as fast as it was filled
By then she knew, just knew, that you were there
You watched from your hiding place as she described you to her friends
You saw her exhaustion and felt something you couldn't define
By the time they found you, you had made yourself at home
Her house had become yours, you walked in her slippers and slept in her bed
She brought people to evict you but you hid until they went away
'They don't know me' you thought – 'they don't know my ways'

Soon she could no longer afford to feed you
One of you was going to have to go and it wouldn't be you
That night, her family and friends prepared her to leave
You watched as the key turned in the lock and the lights went out
You realised what it was that you had felt and couldn't define

You were trapped

This piece (I can't really call it a poem) is about the hallmarks of cancer, a disease we cannot cure until we fully comprehend. What motivates a hooligan who infests a host and dies with it?

Dr Sarah Blagden

Sarah Blagden has been Associate Professor of Experimental Cancer Therapeutics in the Department of Oncology since 2015 at the University of Oxford, and she was my beloved Consultant at Hammersmith Hospital and with Prof Hani Gabra and Prof Christina Fotopoulou have literally saved and extended my life. How do I express my gratitude? By living!

For You All

You've saved my life
Consultant 1, Consultant 2
You've extended my life
Surgeon 1, Surgeon 2,
You've given me back my life,
Miracles of science and courage
Researcher 1, Researcher 2
I thank you more than words could say
You've created my life
Everlasting lineage
Father 1, Mother 2
You've cherished my life
You've encouraged my life
Sister 1, brother 2
Tenderness of creation
Shared genes and blood
You've valued my life
Boisterous and witty
Friend 1, Friend 2
You've respected my unpredictability
You've made my life
You've calmed my life
You've loved my life
Husband 1, husband 2
You've kept me sane
You are so wise, genuine, true.
You've taught me the now
Meditator 1 meditator 2
You've energised my life
Tennis Racquet 1, camera 2
You've enriched my life
Paintbrush 3, Journal 4
You are my life
Full of love
Eloquent and still
Child 1, child 2
Talented and creative
The Joker's hand
Puffins and turtle doves,
Sensitive and ingenious
I love you
You are my life
I thank you all more than words can say

Florence Wilks

A Summer Inconvenience

Routine mammogram,

What a bore!

I suppose I had better go.

Nothing to fear,

They're always clear,

But somehow, you never know.

Recall

Biopsy

The dreaded news.

Surgery

Biopsy

Hear the surgeon's views.

'You're healing well'

'Margins are clear'

'Tennis? Yes! Life goes on.'

Minimal treatment,

Feeling very fortunate,

An inconvenience, nothing on which to dwell.

Early diagnosis,

Swift intervention,

The system is working well.

Polly Kaufmann

Stay

You move to my caress, I feel your heartbeat

Your warmth undresses me and your smile rebuilds my breathing

I need you ... stay ...

Stay to remember the moment our lips met in that first kiss

Stay for the promises that eternity will be you and me

I need you... stay ...

Stay for the tattoo your fingertips ink on my skin

Stay for the passion we can share in the still of night

I need you... stay ...

Stay because of the hole in your heart if I leave

Stay for the forgiveness you give me even though circumstances defy us

I need you... stay ...

Stay for the pain that keeps me in slavery and the pride with which you punish me

Stay because I miss you more than I ever could imagine

I need you... stay ...

My body is yours always

I would crawl over broken glass to be with you again

Stay...

Andrea Richardson

Working on Making it Yours

Flo go with flow

flow where it takes you

Flo you go where it does

where is not knowing where next

but you make it work

working on making it yours

yours is the way

the way to go

we all have a flow

it takes us places we never knew were there

but there is where we find our flow takes us

Surprise awaits for us all where ever we go

for only by going do we find

find what?

we wont know without going there

but we do know that with an open heart

and an open mind

adventure and fun will always accompany on our flow

Flo you rock

if we all flowed a little more like you

we will all with open eyes leave a trodden path of love and happiness

love and happiness

now isn't that a great place to be.

Written for Florence Wilks

Stephen Davies

Keep on Shining

Strong, determined , crazy,
Loving, silly, kind,
Sun, travel, beauty,
Peace meditation, mind,
Venice, Bagni di Luca, Barbados
Small bridges, mountains, white sand,
Richmond, Victoria and Albert, London chaos
Long walks, architecture, a beautiful land,
Thick mattress, deep sofa,
Friendly chatty neighbour
Little dog, two seater
Special family member
Here are collected all the stars
Shining bright from afar
Creating the Milky Way that you are
Continue doing what you do best
Keep on shining from the rest

Hannah Wilks

Two Beauties

Hannah Rose
Daniel Jack
Two beauties
Compassion and breadth
Love no greater
Proud no prouder
Modest talent
Grit and determination
Individuality and beautiful spirit
Creativity and cheeky humour
Even though you are away
You are always with me
When I am away
I will always be with you
Your guardian angel
I love you my babies
You make my world
You are my world
How blessed I am
You two beauties

Florence Wilks

Dandelion Clock

I've been waiting.
Ever quiet.
Swaying gently,
slightly bending,
never breaking.
for the wind.
Sunlight kissed me.
I unravelled.
Richly coloured golden skin.
But the thorns of bigger roses,
stole my light
and boxed me in.
In the distance.
Constant rhythms.
Ticks away my yesterday.
Heavy rooted,
in the shadows.
Close my eyes and float away.
Slowly.
As I'm held here. Stagnant.
Mother nature steals from me.
Takes away my golden splendour,
paints me,
feathered ivory.
Take me! Wind.
Do your damnedest.
Pluck me from this hole this hell.

I'm still waiting.
Ever patient.
Gently swaying,
Slightly bending,
Never breaking.
Ever quiet.
Waiting for the wind.

Marsha Arthurworrey

The Beauty of a Flower

The beauty of a flower

It's petals dressed in dew

Is a small gift, from God, for me and you.

He hopes that we will notice

The effort that He's made

To see so many flowers

Standing on parade.

The colours can be varied

The petals, different sizes

On long stems, carried

As every day arises

With such variations

And colours there to view

A reminder of God's love for me and you.

If only we would stop and stare

Take a moment, to agree.

What beauty there is

In a flower, for all to see.

Not only to appreciate

His exquisite skill and care

But to give us all a rest

And the ability to stare

At a tiny flower, so perfectly dressed

And to thank God, for giving us His best.

Helen Vipond

Where Great Skuas Fly

Her jutting rocks, up high where leaves of gold, of green.
Where Great Skuas dare to fly and nest their eggs.
Where seas are screaming, 'she's alive!' and wild.
Even driving rain can't dampen down her fiery heart inside.

Where mountains stand as proud as men.
Her magic weaves disturbing spells.
She has a hold and won't release you,
tangled tight within her web.

And she may hiss and throw her rocks,
upon her frilly jagged edge,
and spin with wind within her skirt,
through palm trees and Atlantic breeze.

But she too kissed that flat calm sea,
and breathed upon that calf now cow.
For she holds all the anger in,
and spins her web and I'm at peace and free.

Marsha Arthurworrey

Life from Water Comes

Life from water comes
Sit by a stream,
See how she greens the banks,
That home voles, kingfisher, dragonflies
Sustains fish
Refreshes birds,
Racing over rocks
Gliding through smooth pebbles
Sparkling in the sun,
Then gently flowing on

———————

Rita Gorham

Fridays at Six

We sit in our first circle, quiet and wary;
Eyeing one another with a gentle curiosity.
We tell our story, briefly, with our public face.
Mindfulness is a peaceful word,
And with Peter as our kindly guide
We start our journey in its foothills.
Have I got the right equipment?
How will I sit here, all 120 minutes of here?
Nothing to do, nowhere to go.
That sounds so simple, yet daunting.
How can this be easy with a headful of thoughts?
What we have in common is a willingness to try.

Through the practice of the weeks,
At home, there's still a linkage.
We each do what we can, and find
The pre-class talk increases,
Giving us renewed commitment.
We start to smile, even to laugh together.
Two hours are now a precious timeless time,
In this suspended gift of Fridays
We trust, accept and then let go.

We have touched down on Lesson 7,
Our journey near its end, the tools are our to keep.
We shall need them again.
Now, nothing to do, nowhere to go
Has a pleasing sound, like those so
Familiar, welcome bells.

Shall we meet again? Oh yes, each
Time we practise, our nourishing words
Will fuse in some mindful universe.
Just one breath in, just one breath out.
The journey's end of our exploring
Will arrive back where we started
And know the place for the first time.
I am thankful to have known you all.
This helpful, necessary time has shown us
The way to find the gift of ourselves.

Ingrid Tunnicliffe

Vienna

O.S-Bahn, S-Bahn,
U-Bahn, Straßenbahn
All take you on your way.
Stadtmitte, Stephansplatz,
Museumsquartier for the Leopold
Schwedenplatz for the Ring Tram.
But on foot through the Graben
To the Dorotheergasse
And to Café Hawelka,
Loved by so many.
Goulash soup, wonderful coffee
And the true taste of Vienna.

Brian Lee (Papa)

Travelling is Good for Your Soul

Travelling is good for your soul, travelling is good for your heart.
It helps you build friendships that can't be torn apart.
Many experiences had with laughter and tears.
Trust, adventure and adversity all while conquering fears.
Empathy, understanding and tolerance fostered.
Always remember the friends that you meet the family you choose.
They will always be there win, draw or lose.
So get out there, be brave and be bold. Sample all that life has to hold!

Jan-Marie Williams

Days are Passing

Days are passing far too quickly
As we watch our children grow
Time spares none to waste on little nothings
No basking in 'yesterday's' glow

Love them and cherish all you have
Never look back with regrets too late
Move forward onto each new day
'Cause times a passer that forgets to wait...

Carole Burton

Barbour and Vans

Why does she sit at the front of the bus,
Is she crazy or one like us,
So sure of ourselves no one begs to differ,
I'm struck by her age and what she has with her.
Is she studying the works of some long dead writer,
Or browsing the world for something much lighter.
There she sits in Barbour and Vans,
At the front of the bus making life plans.
Does she realise these seats are reserved for the brave,
Those who observe how the others behave.
With her fierce concentration no need to engage,
She is just like us and simply coming of age!

David Alderton

October Half-term Week After Retirement

Children on the transport
Builders at the brickwork
Noise for the neighbours
Dust in the dining-room
Scratching and scraping
Pointing and painting...
STOP the world and
GIVE ME A BREAK!

This morning as the sun grew stronger
I sat within a secret garden.
No shoppers or traffic
Disturbed my peace
Or the garden's mellow fruitfulness.
As Keats once said
And I once read
At my father's funeral
Not so long ago.

Alison Germany

Forever Whispering to You

The world is noisy
but I will be forever
whispering to you!

Sarah-Jane Rodgers

An Empty Seat

First day nerves, feeling reserved
So many bland faces
Looking around, with a signature frown
Both there, of all the places

An empty seat, a look so sweet
Cloaked in mystery
Who was to know, through highs and lows
The rest would be history

Quickly became friends
Burnt the candle at both ends
Had fun being just you and me
Sharing worries, and durries
Teaching you to cook curry
Being silly, and young, and free

I teased you, abused you
You laughed at my new shoes
And that was a part of our charm
Always, whenever, you stayed there
Keeping me away from all the harm

We laughed, and I cried
You wiped tears from my eyes
Then things went rather awry
Everything went wrong
Too soon, he was gone
Prematurely taken up to the sky

I hid in my bed
Didn't do what you said
Went to live in a cocoon
Not meant to be, but accidentally
If anything, just opportune

Time went by. We both tried
Life went on and on
But not a day passed
Without seeing your eyes
Missing you now you were gone

The years, they flew by
We both lived our own lives
Worth began to fade
Then one day in the park
We stayed 'til it got dark
10 years just melted away

There were more tears, more laughter
And through a disaster
You became my man
Now we're back to our old ways,
We argue, on most days
Playing word games and sharing life's plan

It's not always fair, but I'll always be there
Looking after you whenever I can
I can't take it away, or keep the feelings at bay
But I'm glad we're back where it began

After so many years, and through so many
tears
It was right in front of my eyes
I love you, my darling
My soul mate, my reason
Always. Until the day that I die.

———————

Jess Champion

Polish Wedding

There was no rain before the wedding; which was a disappointment.

The festive umbrellas stayed demurely covered;

like shy brides.

Descending marble steps in couples comes the real bride; cool and lithe in blue slacks and wedding brogues, smiling wider and hugging harder than those who more lightly tripped down the aisle expect.

Upstairs, we wait till Mama Cass announces it is time, then watch the bride, veil finally lifted, turn her radiant face to welcome the beauty in white arriving at her side.

Outside after all is changed.

Drops of rain spit; the next party waits beneath John Knox. Women in heels and fascinators slide fascinated eyes in our direction, and all look down in bronzed disapproval.

But this is our moment.

As cameras flash umbrellas unsheathe and joyfully thrust their rainbow colours at the Edinburgh sky.

'Thank you Edinburg' the bride's wife calls out.

As the hard 'g' trips up her unfamiliar tongue, we cheer and wave our colourful banners; remembering their defiant challenge is aimed at darker more forbidding skies.

Kay Stonham

I'm Soon to be a Mother

I was a more science and maths girl
I thought the human body was amazing
I'm in the right place now
I've always wanted to work in a hospital
To give birth in the same hospital
I'm wiser now
I'm soon to be a mother.

Fatuma Mohamed

Pane

Walking through the shops.
Bashed my head on a window.
One hell of a pane.

Brilliant Yellow Sun

Autumnal morning;
Bright yellow sun, falling leaves.
Thoughts turn to winter.

Work Life Balance

Early mornings. Long days.
Working without a break. Where's
The work-life balance?

Jo Glass

Have You Heard the Quiet?

Listen!
To the falling of a leaf,
the crawling of an ant,
the breeze of a midsummer's day

Listen!
To the falling of a snowflake
the soaring of an eagle
the running of a slow small stream
the still of the middle of the night

Listen!
Listen and hear the quiet.

─────────────

Evelyn Joseph

I am the Placebo

I am the placebo
Making my mind matter
I lie in meditation
As the needle is removed from the port
The gauze the only reminder of
What has been, will be, will become
The Avastin that works dually
With my self healing

Florence Wilks

FUCK IT!

(For your notes)

Angels

Some people are not like others
They stand out from the rest
A light shines from within them
They really are the best!

Some people are like angels
Sent from up above
Their kindness will support you
And remind you how to love

There Are No Words

I don't have words
to explain
the misery and grief
when he went away

My longing heart
beating still
disconnected from life
when he went away

Deirdre Fitzgerald

I've Lost

I've lost, oh I have lost
A scarf, a hat, a glove
The page, the thread, the plot
A race, a game, a fight
A job, a house, a home
My friend, my wife, my lover
Memory, hearing, sight
An openness to grieve

But I lose not the will
Because if this life
I am not losing it!

John Wilks

I'm Clean (song)

I'm clean
I wash my hands in your sink
I'm clean
No drugs and no drink
I'm clean
My skin is all pink
I'm clean
But you don't know what I think

David Sinclair

The First Lesson

The first lesson was taught by Eve
When I was too young for questions
She taught me that a woman should be obedient
Should always follow If not there would be consequences
If not there would be blame
Her word was gospel
And so I am silent
Silent when I am described as abrupt, whilst he, ambitious
Silent when I am given less for the same

Silent Helen taught the second lesson
It was you, who spoke of the greatest asset a woman can possess
The only one of value
You showed me that we must not talk about what lurks behind perfection
The pinches and pricks
The coats and layers
The spray and grease
And diligently I slaver my skin, pull my hair, scrub my body
Every morning
To be acceptable

It was Jack who taught the final lesson
For there always has to be a man;
The slayer of women.
He emphasized Eve and clarified Helen,
He showed me that empowerment is not mine to have,
It is to be given to me
It is to be regulated
Or it will be taken

Jessica Richards

Student Nurse – Time

Time.

Time to wake up and get on the correct bus in the dark of the early morning.

Time to wake others, people you will be caring for that day.

Time to feed others and help, help others to live through their daily activities.

Time feed yourself, keeping fit, to help the fighting.

Time to conquer, conquer fear of all.

Time to reflect on how that fear, a fear that should not be feared.

Time to stop, stop standing.

Time to get on the correct bus in the dark of night.

Time to sleep knowing that fear is happening every 5 seconds.

Poppy Richardson

Train

I let the train carry me
Waiting for time to pass,
Trying to fill my mind with nothing but he,
How foolish to think it would last.

I told us over and over
at Christmas that it was not meant to be.
In my stomach I knew when sober,
that right now we couldn't be happy.

The weekend in Oxford I stayed,
him and I skin to skin.
but knowing the decision already made,
no solution were I to win.

Four long years we'd lasted,
before I called it quits.
The havoc that entailed when parted,
brings emotion that never quite sits.

Since then we've moved on and forward,
His confidence grown leaps and bounds,
for this I am so happy
and my love I have newly found.

But now, how cruel to have my hopes risen,
to act like everything were back on track.
Those kind words I'd sit there and listen,
which now have been taken aback.

However, Oxford I've gone,
our business is now done.
My final farewell has been made
and our future is still yet to be played.

Hannah Wilks

Ealing Common (song)

There's a man on the common
Playing the saxophone
A long way to travel
For a room to call his own
Brings a pain in my heart
Where you used to be
And it's starting to get the better of me

There are two hearts broken on the common tonight
One is singing for dear life, the other playing to survive
And we're come to the common to find some common ground
Need space to be on your own, you're not alone.

Bridget Chapple

Requiescat in Pace

Bury my bones by the A316.

Not for me the lofty ridge,

the watery place,

the bosky space.

Spare my ash from fish or fowl,

from creeping things,

from fox or owl.

No rustic plot.

No funeral pyre.

Just lay me down beneath the tyre.

Tim Whitehead

Dad Follows St Peter into the Garden of Heaven

'Well, here we are. This is your plot.
I think you'll find it all reminds
you of your last one, your last life.'
Consults his clipboard, clears his throat,
ticks each one off the list He wrote :
'Five rows of spuds, three of leeks,
five of onions - good to keep -
beetroot 'Bolthardy?' - I think that's right -
cabbages dark green and white,
carrots three and parsnips four,
runner bean wigwams proud and tall.
You never were one for fancy breeds
or greenhouses or foreign seeds.
This will get you started then.
And if you're lost or need a hand,
there's kin a plenty - look around.'

And off he goes. Pleased. Job done.

Then...
Along the path, past pristine veg,
with sandy hair restored he treads.
Ben clasps his son, who hugs him back
and breathes him in and laughs and laughs.
'Hello lad. You took your time!
How've you been? Has life been kind?
Your patch and mine are one you see,
so I'm here for you as you were for me.
It won't take long to settle in,
mind you, that's not a problem now.
Arthur's here, look, back from France,
subdued perhaps, his spirit broken -
in all this time he's hardly spoken -
but it's good to have my brother near.
I chat at him and in reply
of sorts he smiles or nods his head
or shakes his paper, as yet unread
and we walk a while.

He doesn't dig of course - afeared of mud -
but he likes the sun upon his face
and when my daily tasks are done
we have a Woodbine, just the one.'

'In Heaven it's as it was on earth!
My garden lives again in all its worth.
I missed that damson, felled to blight,
but here transcended, bathed in light.
Victoria plum and egg plum too,
gooseberries,apples rhubarb... Oh...
But what about the pie?
I need my wife.
Will she be here?'
A gentle pause.

'No. Not this year.
Your lass has too much living yet
and cakes to bake and men to raise.
Your job now is to prepare
the ground and all that it surrounds
and plant and weed and prune and care.
The weather's clement here you'll find.'

Strong again, spine straight and true,
stripped to the waist, he digs and digs,
hard belly tiger-striped with tan,
his skin unmarked by needle stabs.
And all the cats he ever loved
bookend the rows with furry grins.
His guardians.

And by and by the seasons drift,
no frost, no drought, no hail, no storms,
no pain, no aches, no cancer worms
its way of ruin. Here we sit.
And by and by are reunited.
Love lives on and on and on
on earth, as it is in Heaven.

Nina Robertson

You're a Miracle

One cell from Dad found
One cell from Mum,
Each one carrying 23 chromosomes,
The one from your Mum
Carrying half her DNA
The one from your Dad
Carrying half of his DNA
These two cells meet
Merging into one single cell

When they did
These chromosomes matched
They began to from together
A brand new DNA code
Using four characters
Four nucleotides
They began to write out
The three billion character description
Of who you are

Scientists say that if you took
The DNA out of that one cell
And stretched it out
That the DNA would be six feet long
So amazing, that if I were to read your DNA
One character per second night and day
It would take me 96 years
Just to read the description
Of you

The that single cell does the amazing
It sets out to build that model of you
Writing and painting a picture
Which has never been written before
In the history of human kind
In the womb
Miracles are happening every moment
At 3 days old
You have 16 cells

That one cell has turned into 16 cells,
In its way to making the
75 billion cells that make up your body
There's so much DNA inside your body
That if you stretched it end to end
There would be enough DNA
To go to the moon and back
178,000 times
We're miracles, you and me.

Catherine Whitfield

BRCA Sisters

I always sensed that
Angelina J and we
Had things in common

Florence Wilks

The Seagull

Stands upon the beach

Its toes and legs in shingle

He looks at me as if to say

'I'm so sad, I'm single

It's lonely here, amongst the stones

A mate I cannot see

Did God create us to be pairs?

If so, where's one for me?

I flew long distance, searching hard

A mate I could not find

I prayed a prayer to God and asked

Please God would you be kind?

To show me where I can go

To bump into a mate

Before I get too old to fly

And it gets too late.

Helen Vipond

Memories

Pebbles on an endless beach
That live beneath my shoe
Rocked, rolled, reeled about
The end a glistening hue

Leaves that scatter the Autumn mist
Glide softly through the air
Crunch, clutter down they go
Lost without a care

The embers of a time forgot
Give way to the open road
Over the fields we dream again
A story yet to be told

Natatja Bauer

Skinny Dipping

Skinny dipping
Banks beer sipping
Love making
Heart breaking
Ain't got a clue, she's only 22

Wedding bells
Belly swells
Baby in tummy
Yummy Mummy
Key to the door... she's 34

New job,
Loads of stress
Lump in breast,
You know the rest

Lumpectomy, radiation
Changing room humiliation
Entry-level mutilation
Glad to be alive!
She's only 35!

Bloated tummy
Laparotomy
Life changer
Life in danger
Oh score!
She's 44!

Reminiscing
Champagne swigging
Shades of grey
Red room of play
Livin' life,
Lovin' it too,
She's healthy, happy
And now she's 52!

Adele Williams Sewell

She Drives Me Crazy

Sultry satins and sensuous silks
Bring to mind one Florence Wilks
Graceful with poise like a young ballerina
I'd have her in the back of a Ford Cortina

Committed to a cause she speaks without fear
Despite her suffering a cost so dear
Her focus and grit show she's very alive
I'd give her a ride in a DB5

Highly principled so there's no surprise
She does what's right without compromise
There's no chance she'd yield to the devil's choice
Of impropriety aboard a white Rolls Royce

Love of family holds pride of place
Shining bright on her beautiful face
Her children's achievements reflect her drive
She's ideal for a jump in my Audi A5

In my mind I see the white dressed dancer
Calm in the face of a dreadful cancer
Bopping away at the Tennis Club beano
Throttling hard a Ferrari Dino

Enjoy her flame that burns so bright
That helps us brave the dark of night
Power and passion delivered gently
Any chance of a bonk in my two door Bentley?

Dick Sands

No One Knows

It is like I am in the autumn of my life
Waiting for the leaves to fall
One by one slowly
Or suddenly all in the blink of an eye
Brown are my days
Lonely, solitary
Russet tinged with the love of family and friends
Winter tightening my shoulder
Waiting, waiting
Stealthily,menacingly
Ready, waiting for a sign,a signal from deep within
How can this be?
Who knows but the cycle of me.

Who Knows, Part 2

Russet tinged with the love of family and friends
A smile, a hug
Kind thoughts across the miles
Small but huge gestures
Moments of forgetting
Living through your eyes, your touch, your words
Just knowing you care
Warmth, life, joy, hope replace despair
Melting the icicles
Keeping winter from my door
Helping me breathe once more
You are all my long glorious summer days
Thank you

Michelle Carter

Being There

To share a bed
Then shave a head
You do what's needed
To take the hits
Then go again
You do what's needed
To see the day!
Then jump for joy
You do what's needed

Steve Poole

On Losing a Loved One

Descend with me to that place
where grief stretches out its tentacles
to grip and enclose you.
Let the tears flow.
Stay there awhile and feel the pain,
the emptiness and the loss.

Ascend now to that place
where you were before.
Handle the band of gold you gave me,
given with love,
given in love,
and know the circle is not broken.
Love has not died, nor ever will.
Grief has now gone
and love lives on.

Alistair Dunlop

We Were Children

Growing.

Try to reach the sky.

Today I heard.

You went down in flames.

Rest in peace, my lost one.

#cold #clouds #fire #sunset #last
#day #lost #childhood #love
#sognogfjordane #norway

Cathrine S Holsen Gardner

Astronomy

Tonight,
While the stars plot their silences,
Which lodge inside my firmament
And stab my sleepless tossing torment
Your smile, like a sliver of moon
Mocks my groping in the gloom
As I stumble forward
Into another reluctant day.

John Green

Treatment No 33 - October 2015

Today I get a bed
Clean sheets
Side room
Reclining chair
Super hot decaf coffee

I have a strange love for this place
As I laze and my heart pumps around
Chemicals for a future life

Tennis shoes off
This silent world
NHS wonderfully evolved for us
Through the windows
(The lucky ones)
Stoically resolved

Pillows high shuffling
From ward to gratitude
And acceptance.

A piece of raw theatre.

Life is short for all of us
But particularly evident here
Being lived
Each moment, slowly, truthfully
Fearless and (un)comfortable

Florence Wilks

Glorious Adventure

This dreadful debilitating life sucking disease
Has turned my life into a
Glorious adventure.
An urgency and truth to life.
I feel very blessed.

Florence Wilks

Nausea

In my world of nausea
I need something to be clear
In my world of nothing
I need something to fear

In my world of stress
I need something to shroud
In my world of silence
I need something to be loud

In my world of perplexity
I need a something to go
In my world of confusion
I need something to show

In my world of love
I want someone to care
In my world of beauty
I want someone to share

Max Child

History

City lights the rush
Rain drops impending hush

Detached from this place
There is a man an empty face

True perception
The chase of perfection

The body has limitations
Soul full of these frustrations

The visionary man
By far the saddest man

May his history be consumed

Max Child

50!! Tennis Court Rules

GTC – it's been said before provides a source of fun
Thru' lobs, volleys, ground strokes to name but only some
We also need to know the rules by which we do abide
So we re-create them in perpetuity by printing them on your (bum) t-shirt!

Karen Dickinson

Tie Break Rules

Tie break rules confuse
Who serves first and from which side
Let's just have a drink

Alison Shindler

So His Brain it did Creak

Young Florence, she came up to Rick,
She said 'Write this poem, and quick',
So his brain it did creak
As rhymes he did seek,
But he just hit a wall made of brick.

Rick Beresford

Limerick for Florence

Our Florence can really thump a ball
With racket in hand she does enthral
With grace and a giggle
A thwack and a wiggle
She is an inspiration to us all

Mike Kaufmann

Tennis

Should I write a poem of tennis
That's not a good idea
I'm not of the Society Mensa
Or anything close, I fear.

Perhaps a word on footballing
I do so love the sport
But my knowledge is really quite galling
To what now do I resort?

I do like playing solitaire
With nary a soul around
I can peek & cheat without a care
And sing with the voice of a hound.

Gilpin Netburn

Childhood memories

Happy and sad childhood memories
Torment me incessantly.
They crowd my thoughts at once,
Yet I keep coming back to one.
I am at home with my dear Daddee[1],
Lying with my head on her shoulder,
On a stuffed mattress on our cow dung floor,
Sharing what we have with our cow Ramu.
'Look at those flashing stars beta[2],'
My Daddee shouts with delight
Pointing at them with her walking stick
Her bony hands hugging me tighter.
How beautiful they looked,
Twinkling and beckoning
Me to leave,
Through the holes in the thatch.
I stared at the stars,
I prayed and wished,
'Please, take me away to the land of plenty,'
With my Daddee always besides me.

[1] Translates as 'granny' in English
[2] Translates as 'son' in English

Jay Woogara

You Don't Know What I'm Thinking

It's nearly a quarter to one and the tables haven't been set yet. Amalia is considering pointing this out to Felix, but curbs herself and remembers that he's been taking in deliveries at the restaurant since very early, while she was still in their bed, rolling into his concave of warmth.

The street door squeaks open on her reverie and a gnarled and ancient head pops slowly round it, like a tortoise looking for lettuce. Amalia wipes her busy face away and replaces it in the blink of an eye with her smiling-at-the-customers face.

When she realises that it is Laurence, Amalia's smile edges into something genuine.

'Lorenzo!', she calls out with gusto and enough enthusiasm to wake him up a bit. You have to do that with the elderly, or they only catch half of what you say.

Laurence notices the bare table, and says, in execrable Spanish, the rough equivalent of: 'Sorry, am I a little early?'

In worse English, Amalia says, 'No problem, Lorenzo! Sit down, sit down.'

Laurence eases himself into his chair, at his small table, which is tucked into a corner. But it is the table he has chosen. He faces outwards, towards the rest of the room, and so it is a vantage point, of sorts. And it is his table, the one he occupies every day, unless he is not in by one fifteen, in which case, by arrangement, they can let the table go. But he is there most days, and sometimes, often, Edith is with him.

'Edita no come today?' asks Amalia.

'No, she's a bit poorly today.' He says this in English. He doesn't have the vocabulary, or the energy, to get the information out any other way. Besides, it's only a polite question. If Edith isn't with him, the reason is apparent enough.

The faltering conversation brings Felix out from the kitchen. 'Lorenzo! Hombre!' Felix claps Laurence on the back, as is the continental way, and though Laurence is, fortunately, seated by now, he feels his teeth give a small jerk forward inside his mouth.

'Oh, hola; hola, Felix.'

Laurence raises a slightly tremulous hand in greeting, and Felix takes hold of it with surprising tenderness. 'Welcome, Lorenzo. Bring the menu.'

'Yes. Thank you. Gracias.'

And off goes Felix, bearing his impressive stomach before him, the epitome of a well-fed Spaniard, a possibility still recent enough to be impressive.

Laurence goes through the motions of looking through the menu, stopping first, as always, at the photo of times long past in this small, ancient town which has come into being between the Mediterranean and a singular mountain, of which the locals and the more recent arrivals are all inordinately fond. The photo shows the restaurant a hundred years before, before cars, before tourism, but still a restaurant, in many incarnations. Before luscious chips cooked in olive oil. Chips with everything. Not here though, at La Casa de Amalia. You have to ask for them. It is a vague embarrassment, potentially, but then, who cares? Who is there to judge a wasted old ex-pat on his eating habits? What a joy, he could jolly well eat asparagus and chips every day if he liked!

This is what he chooses. He casts one last glance at the picture on the front of the menu and pats it. The spire of the fortress church rises eternal in the background. Perhaps he will visit it after lunch, for the peace his atheistic heart will feel in its interior, Spartan after the ravages of the Civil War, almost beyond memory now. But Laurence remembers.

He is very old, and for this reason he decides that he will probably not walk to the church this afternoon. Though the almond blossom is everywhere a delight to the eye, it is wondrous cold, which is why he is at his inside table. In spring, summer and autumn, he and Edith have an outside table too, tucked away as discreetly as possible on the terrace, which gives onto a pretty square with a fountain. Now, in February, only small balls of rolled leaves and dust populate the exterior. From the terrace, he can see the front door of their apartment block down the road, above the bank, and their balcony, but from here, indoors, it is invisible. Just as well. If he cannot see the door and the balcony, then somehow he doesn't have to imagine Edith making her way laboriously around their small apartment, her knuckles white where she clutches her Zimmer frame for dear life, the shield between her and a bad fall.

These are the places he now calls home. He and Edith.

The following day they are both there, Laurence first, Edith some ten minutes later. She likes to make her own way there in her own time, scrape her frame along those 500 yards of her independence which mean that she continues to live. As she shuffles through the door of La Casa de Amalia, Laurence rises to help her to her seat, tucking the frame out of the way.

'I think it's sweet, the way they sit there quietly together,' says Felix from behind the bar, where he is shining glasses with a tea towel.

'Yes, companionable silence, after so many years.' Amalia smiles in their direction.

'I wonder if we'll become like that?'

'What? Silent? I can't see that, can you?', she laughs.

'Well, I mean, happy just to sit there. That's what I mean.'

'Hmm.'

'What?'

'You don't think it's that they don't like each other anymore, do you? That they don't want to speak to each other? Is that what happens?' Amalia shoots Felix a worried look.

'No, silly, no,' he says. 'If anything, they may just have run out of things to say to each other.'

'I suppose so...'

'I mean, after you've discussed politics, global warming, corruption, whatever, for fifty years, well, you've probably said everything you've got to say on the matter!'

'And they're so old, I suppose most of their friends have died, poor things...'

'That's a bit depressing, Amalia. Maybe they're thinking about all the things they've done in their lives. You know, going over them again. Remembering.'

'You're such an optimist, aren't you?'

'Someone's got to do it.' He throws his hands out and grins as the tea towel flies across the bar. 'Go on, take their bread over before they faint from hunger.'

Amalia smiles and makes her way over to the antediluvian couple, placing a wicker basket of warm bread on their table and a small pot of alioli.

'Good days, Edita, how you?'

Edith's Spanish is more lamentable still than Laurence's, so she confines herself to her native tongue, distant in place and memory as Blighty is. 'Fine, thank you, dear. As well as can be expected.'

Amalia is unsure of what Edith is saying, so she smiles at her and, impulsively, because in Spain the elderly are still a wrinkled miracle and a treasure to be loved, kisses her on the cheek. It is as soft as the skin of a peach.

Edith looks a little surprised, but is not displeased. She has become accommodated, now, to the cult of the old. She rather likes it and reaches up to stroke Amalia's cheek. She cannot reach to kiss her, or rather, to do so would necessitate a small military operation involving the frame and its retrieval.

Laurence has remained more English, more reserved. He watches as people, the locals, treat him with the deference due to an avuncular old codger, observes them as they assume that he is the amiable relic of a bygone age and empire. But they do not know him.

'Maybe there's been a tragedy, maybe that's why they're so quiet,' says Amalia as she returns to the kitchen hatch at the end of the bar. 'Oh! Maybe they lost a child!'

'And their apartment's a shrine to it, with pictures everywhere and gaudy plastic flowers around them, no?'

'Stop it! I didn't mean that! It's just that they never have anyone with them. Not like the other foreigners. No friends, no relatives... no children.'

'Maybe they weren't able to have children,' says Felix with a frown. This is unthinkable to him, the joy at the other end of the age spectrum, one day. Soon, hopefully, though he hasn't quite dared raise the topic yet.

'Poor things,' says Amalia.

Felix smiles inwardly; it is a good sign.

On Mondays, La Casa de Amalia closes, to give the staff a rest. They cannot be replaced, as, like all the local restaurants, they are family run. On this day, Amalia and Felix do what they please, and this particular Monday they have decided to take a stroll round the old town, walk the narrow cobbles between the high old sandstone houses, see who they bump into and stop to pass the time with. They walk hand in hand, arms swinging, and from time to time exchange a small, affirming kiss.

Passing the huge panelled doors of the church, they are most surprised to see Laurence emerging.

'Lorenzo! What surprise!' says Amalia, reaching out her arms for the customary two kisses and arm squeeze. 'You like the church? You go mass?'

Laurence smiles, and they realise, of a sudden, that this is unusual. He is not an angry man, just serious.

'No, no,' says Laurence, 'it's just peaceful in there. Oddly enough.'

'Si, si.' They echo, quizzically.

Laurence looks at them: the happy young couple. They don't know. But perhaps they should. Perhaps they would want to know. He sighs so deeply that Felix reaches towards him.

'Are you OK, Lorenzo?'

'Yes, yes. I was just thinking... Look, come with me.' And with uncustomary vigour Laurence leads them to the side of the church. He points up at the pockmarks spattered high up on the side wall, illuminated by an early morning, spring sun. 'You see that?' says Laurence, 'those marks on the wall?'

'Si, si.' Amalia and Felix echo once more, exchanging glances.

'This church has stood for a thousand years, but those marks are not from the time of the Moors. Or from medieval battles, or pirates. None of that. Do you know when those marks were made?'

Amalia and Felix shake their heads.

'The Civil War.' Laurence's jaw sets. 'During the Spanish Civil War. The Republicans fought hard against the advance of the Nationalists, here.' He points emphatically to the ground. 'It was one of the last places to fall. Did you know?'

More shaking of heads, slowly now.

'At the end, the Republicans took refuge in the church, and the Nationalists tried to winkle them out with rocket launchers. See?' Laurence turns away from them and points again at the marks of violence.

'I have no idea, Lorenzo. I have no idea this happen,' says Amalia

'No, neither me,' says Felix.

'But how this you know?' says Amalia.

Laurence looks back at them and his eyes are swimming with unshed tears and he says: 'Because I was there. I was in the church with them. I was one of the International Brigadiers.' And he covers his eyes so that they will not see his emotion.

'Oh, Lorenzo,' says Amalia, stroking his arm. 'You fight for us. For Spain.' Suddenly, she, too, is overcome, roused by her slightly dormant left-wing sympathies and simple compassion.

Felix, unable at the best of times to see a loved one upset, and bearer as he is of a very soft heart, follows. 'Come,' he says, 'we take walk. We walk together.' And off they go, slowly through the waking town, Laurence in the middle, Amalia and Felix either side of him, their young arms through his thin ones. He permits this, and they do not speak for quite a while.

To himself, he keeps the knowledge that Edith, who is almost certainly shuffling from one side of their living room to the other and who is, he knows, fading, made a decision. They both did. As one war slid consequentially into another and there was no room for their ideology of freedom and democracy, they decided that it was no world to bring children into. It is a sadness that lies between them, a lacuna of loss, of regret.

The following week, as Laurence is about to settle himself in and await the arrival of Edith, he spots something on the wall above his chair.

When she arrives, he points at it. 'Edie, look.'

In a gilded frame is a small reproduction of the flag of the Second Republic, the lower red stripe of today replaced by yesterday's brilliant purple. Amalia approaches, her face a little set. She has had a row with Felix, who is afraid that some of their customers might object, to which she has countered, definitively, that they can go elsewhere then.

Laurence raises his wobbly right fist in salute and Amalia face softens as she hands them the menus.

Laurence looks at the picture on the cover, 'La Casa del Pueblo. The House of the People. That was its name' he says.

——————

Elena Soto

The Hanwell Gardener

——————————

Tools flung randomly into the Estate
The Hanwell gardener sets off in search of greenery to tame
Happily as Mother Nature reigns supreme
It is a blissfully circular routine.

——————————

Cilla Hilton-Jones

The Ramblings of a Facebook Idiot

- Just can't find that new cliché.
- Just can't get enough minimalism.
- Passionately without purpose.
- In possession of a purely decorative conscience.
- A drawer of keys that fit no lock, that's what longevity means my friends.
- Is stirring up apathy.
- Really should reconcile his net income with his gross habits.
- When she said 'you have issues', I heard 'tissues' so offered up my handkerchief.
- When she said I was a 'right tool' I was quite proud to be thought of as useful... at first.
- Had a letter from Screwfix informing me they are not a dating agency.
- Threw my hands up in despair, lucky they were attached or would have lost them too.
- Deprivity – the absence of a public convenience when desperately required.
- Got my pyjamas out of the drawer and called them lounge pants and top, trendy again at no extra cost.
- Saw the Bayeux Tapestry online through the interweb and am stunned at the technical advancements of 11th century... who knew they knew how to post online?
- Need to get a chair next to my bed so I can have a rest when I first get up.
- Turns out a fable isn't a folding table after all.
- When one's partner bemoans not having an eye level grill, it is not acceptable to retort that if she got on her knees she would have one, even when one thinks one is being witty I am told.
- Who knew an ilk was not a sick elk?
- Whilst waiting at the gates to Green Park yester eve a charming chap asked if I was on Grinder?, 'Why no' replied I, 'but I did get my haircut today'.

_____

Oksob

Glazed Over

Purposefully she drew back the curtains and surveyed the street below. She called it her sniper window. She saw herself donning her Lycra balaclava and silently taking out the threats to suburban security, or perhaps just the foxes. Or the dawdlers.

People had routines in the morning, whether they wanted them or not. It was something she'd liked about getting older, the comfort of certainty. Others could set their watches by her: drawing her curtains, setting the coffee to deliver one meticulous cup, measuring out her muesli, spoonful by careful spoonful, half an apple, seven almonds. Never eight. If she'd gone to clean, and floss, her teeth by the time you walked past, you'd know you'd missed your train. Only by a minute. It wouldn't bother you like it would her.

And so the small crystals of glass spattered on the windowsill startled her. She picked one up and held it to the light, narrowing her eyes. It looked like coarse sea salt. The sort people brought her back from holidays in the south of France, knowing she didn't do nougat. Saline. No. Adamantine. A fine word, adamantine. Hard. She made a mental note to use it at her book club on the first Thursday in October.

She was puzzled, as well as done with finding the mot juste, which had afforded her a disproportionate satisfaction. (Puzzled pedant seeks like-minded methodologist for Punctual Friendship and Timed Scrabble Games). Puzzled, she looked up at the window, and in particular, at the small hole that had appeared there since last night. Was it vandals? She shuddered. Spontaneous combustion? She shuddered again. Spontaneity was so unsettling.

She'd need a glazer. Or was it a glazier? Not a Paul Michael Glaser who'd skid to a halt in his red Ford Gran Torino and abandon it at an angle in Dreardon Road. That always used to annoy her slightly, even back then. She imagined parallel parking it for him while he got to work with the putty. Her sister had Starsky on her bedroom wall. She had to make do with David Soul, whom she pretended to prefer and proved it by playing Don't Give up on Us, Baby on repeat. But Starsky was the real deal. All cross-eyed and chunky cardigan. He'd be ancient by now. And probably incapable of fixing her window. She'd need a local guy with a one-syllable name and a ladder.

Jack turned up at 12.18.

'The trouble with it is…', he began, 'we get a lot of this, especially in the summer. Kids. They're bored, aren't they?'

She nodded, mutely.

'Hah!' he said, hoisting up his jeans for reasons best known to himself, and leaning onto her worktop. She'd polish that after he'd gone. 'In my day, we'd have got a clip round the ear from the old man. I'd have 'em cleaning up the riverbank in their holidays.'

She wondered what his profile might look like. Interests: transparency, justice, educational development. The capacity to lead people up that online garden path was boundless. The impassioned impasse. The colossal cyber cul-de-sac. She considered adding alliteration to her own profile under hobbies.

Jack set to work. By 12.41 he'd relieved her of her broken window, forty quid and the will to go on living. He paused and turned, Columbo-style, at the front gate.

'Oh!' he said, 'I forgot to say. I found this on the floor by your bedroom window.'

He held up a small silver cylinder, the size of a kidney bean.

Jackie Naffah

Maria's Half Pound Cake

The easiest fruit cake you will ever make and it always tastes great even if it sinks a bit!

I had a lovely email from Florence asking for contributions to her collection of thoughts and musings. I then spent a happy half hour regretting that I so readily agreed to put pen to paper. I realised almost the same moment that I said yes that I had nothing much to share except a cracking and easy cake recipe which has got me out of trouble on many occasions so, in best Bake Off spirit, here goes!

Ingredients

- 1/2 lb (225g) self raising flour either (white or wholemeal)
- 1/2 lb (225g) caster sugar
- 1/2 lb (225g) butter
- 1/2 lb (225g) mixed dried fruit
- 1/4 lb (115g) nuts – pecans are especially nice
- 1/4 lb (115g) cherries, dates or stoned prunes
- 3 eggs
- 1 teaspoon vanilla essence
- 100 ml milk
- 8' round or square cake tin

Method

1. Preheat oven to Gas Mark 3 (170°C / 325°F)

2. Grease your cake tin and line with baking paper

3. Beat the butter and sugar together until smooth

4. Beat the eggs and add them to the sugar and butter

5. Add the vanilla essence and beat it into the mix

6. Sift the flour into the bowl and cream the mix together adding the milk if it is too stiff

7. When the flour is all mixed in add the fruit and nuts and mix it all together

8. Pour the mix into the prepared tin and bake at for about an hour. The cake is cooked when you can put a knife in and it comes out clean but don't open the oven until at least half an hour is gone or it really will sink. When it is cooked let it cool down in the oven.

9. To be honest you have to do that last bit or someone will try and it eat while it is still hot! You can also use the same recipe but make buns instead of one cake. Cook for a shorter time.

Maria Murtagh

Born in Early Half

Born in early half,
an unfinished carved virgin.
Only land survives.

James Nawka

Blackbird

blackbird announcement
heralding my departure
shrill melody

Steph Robertshaw

Every New Petal a Flowering Force

The fuchsia is formidable
Every new petal a flowering force
Each with a unique colour and shade
As one fades or battles against cold wind and rain
A new layer appears to open up into the sun
And when I think they have all gone
Overnight the fuchsias have gathered strength and are re-born
As winter approaches my fuchsias fight in red, orange and white
On a cold day in a dark garden they are asleep in a warm purple berry
to tell me they will be back next year
Now I know why the fuchsia was my mum's favourite flower

Barbara Jamison

London

I love you London,
With your beauty and your grace
You wrap me in your arms and
Keep me warm and safe.

I walk your streets full of wealth and gold
With people rushing by
But turn the corner
of your streets and cry, cry, cry

The poverty and sadness that prevails
In every corner I go by
People begging and kneeling
As others rush on by.

Marie Martinez-Negrillo

Book Group Questions for Youngsters

1. Read aloud poems *Summer* by Olivia Maieli (pg 7), and *Autumn* by Zoe Cardy (pg 7). Which is your favourite season? Which is your favourite line in each poem? Can you draw a picture of your favourite place and season?

2. Read aloud the poem *Dylan Thomas* by Maurice Chapple Wise (pg 13). One of the lines is 'Where the weather often gales', what do you think this means? How would you describe today's weather? Do you like poems that rhyme? Can you write one about today's weather?

3. Read aloud the poem *Heavenly Father* by Lukasz Sloma (pg 8). How does it make you feel? Do you know what the word 'compassion' means. Can you find it in a dictionary? What image in your head do you get when you think of the word 'love'? What colour is love for you? Name three places you love.

4. Read *Midnight Fox* by Maisie Duff (pg 12). Have you read the book *Midnight Fox* by Betsy Byars? What do you think the lines 'Regal and beautiful, she stalks through the night, a tail with such beauty, eyes black as coal' mean? Could you draw a picture of her from this description? Try! What colour are your eyes? Your mum and dad's eyes? How would you describe them?

5. Read aloud *A Recipe For Friendship* by Georgie Greig (pg 11). Do you have a best friend? Could you write a poem to him/her? What is your favourite recipe?

6. Read aloud *About Tracey/Fairy* by Audrey Tsantilis-Lodge, aged 7 (pg 9). The poem is about her Fairy Godmother, Tracey Weatherill, who died. It is a beautiful poem, full of sunshine. Which is your favourite verse? Do you have a person who is very special to you? Can you describe them in five words? Could you write a poem about your special person? Do you enjoy handwriting? Or do you prefer typing on the computer?

7. Read *Maria's Half Pound Cake*, by Maria Murtagh (pg 96), can you make this cake with an adult?

8. Read *Breakfast* by Barney Judic Golden Retriever (pg 15) and *Fred and George* by Andrew Lee (pg 14). Can you imagine being Barney, Fred or George? Do you have a pet? What is your favourite animal? Find a picture of a puffin and turtle dove. If you could be any animal what would you be?

9. Read *Joe-isms* by Joseph Daire Arthurworrey (pg 10). Do you like his drawing? Have you any drawings you did when you were younger? Which 'Joe-ism' do you find the most amusing? Can you remember funny things you might have said or done when you were little?

Book Group Questions for Adults

I hope you agree that this is a wonderful collection of short stories, musings on life and poetry. I love the fact that people who said they could never write a poem have, and they are even more lovely because of that. I did a course called 'The Healing Journey' at Paul's Cancer Support Centre in Clapham, and they taught us that journalling, as well as meditation and visualisation, are good ways of dealing with the stress of cancer. I always carry around a journal with me, writing snippets of my feelings and reactions/thoughts etc. I would recommend it to all people. Writing is a way of self soothing. Reading a way of broadening our minds and understanding others, as well as just a gorgeous and luxurious way to spend the time, slipping away into our imagination.

Both poems and short stories combine meaning, emotion, language and images. They contains rhythm and sound with sight and ideas. All at once it appealing to the senses, feelings and the mind. Working together even when the parts seem to exist separately.

You could read with a pencil in your hand. Mark it up; write in the margins; react to it; get involved with it. Circle important, or striking, or repeated words. Draw lines to connect related ideas. Mark difficult or confusing words, lines, and passages.

Read through the piece, several times if you can, both silently and aloud.

These questions could be used as prompts.

1. Compare *Poem of Love* by Diana Hunter (pg 34) with *An Empty Seat* by Jess Champion (pg 54). They are beautiful poems written from the heart. As Thomas Hardy said: 'The poet should touch our hearts by showing his own.'. What questions would you ask Diana or Jess if you had the chance?

2. Read *Polish Wedding* by Kay Stonham (pg 56). How do you interpret the opening line 'There was no rain before the wedding; which was a disappointment.'? Why do you think Kay says it was a disappointment? I love the line 'The festive umbrellas stayed demurely covered; like shy brides'. Which is your favourite line? What do you think is meant by the last line?

3. Read *No One Knows* and *Who Knows Part 2* by Michelle Carter (pg 76). What feelings are expressed? Can you find words to describe how reading these poems make you feel? Compare the first poem with Part 2.

4. Read *Life Achievements* by Jay Woogara (pg 17), and *Friendship* by Elaine Hill (pg 19). What are your favourite lines? How are the poems similar? What do they tell us about Jay and Elaine?

5. Read aloud *Skinny Dipping* by Adele Williams Sewell (pg 74), and *She Drives me Crazy* by Dick Sands (pg 75). Which verses are your favourite? Both cheeky and funny, witty and entertaining. Rather than discuss, chat about these poems.